The Better o' a Sang

Jim Reid

Scottish
Arts Council

Published by Taigh na Teud
13 Upper Breakish
Isle of Skye
IV42 8PY
Scotland
info@scotlandsmusic.com
www.scotlandsmusic.com

Typeset and designed at Angus Digital Media Centre,
Brechin Business Park, Brechin DD9 6RJ
www.admc.tv

Music transcribed by Colin Douglas and Christine Martin

Printed by Bell & Bain Limited, 303 Burnfield Road,
Thornliebank, Glasgow G46 7UQ

Author's Acknowledgements

I want to thank all of the following people. The late Belle Stewart for 'Loch Duich' and her 'Business Card' poem; the late Mrs C.Geddes who, after her husband's death, gave me all Chae's music because, as she said, "He tell't me tae mind and dae it"; Jim Ramsay for the tune 'The Taysiders'; Bert Murray for all the occasions when he played with us, and for his tune 'The Foundry Band'; the Wylie's of Harray for allowing us to take the framed music off the wall and copy it, then allowing me to include it in this collection; my 'guiding lights' most of whom are now extinguished – Jimmy McBeath, Davy Stewart, Jeanie Robertson, Cameron Turriff, Charlie Murray, Alex Campbell, Matt McGinn, Hamish Imlach, Norman Buchan, Ewan McColl, Mary Brooksbank; Pete Shepheard who first realised that we were worth recording and took on the almost impossible task of organising us in a recording studio. A good few of the songs and tunes in this book have been recorded by him on Springthyme Records, Balmacolm, Fife; Bob Reid for his tune 'Marag Cnocach', but mostly for having, for all of our lives, virtually the same likes and dislikes, which has been a great encouragement along the road, so far; Julia Crawford, without whom I would never have compiled this collection.

I also wish to thank Angus Council Cultural Services for permission to reproduce the photograph of Violet Jacob (1863-1946) on page 50.

Photograph of Huband/Reid on page 91 reproduced with kind permission of Pete Boardman.

Introduction   by Billy Kaye

I mind the first time I visited the Foundry Bar in Arbroath. The place wes steiran an the music had sic virr an smeddum, it gart yer feet tap and yer hert lowp wi joy at bein alive. At the storm centre o it aw wes Jim Reid, shouthers hunched an heid ower the guitar, drivin on the rhythm o reels an mairches. I had come from Edinburgh, where every young musician seemed to have a repertoire consisting of Planxty's or the Bothy Band's greatest hits learned off disc and repeated with monotonous regularity. Now I was hearing Scottish music rooted in the Angus countryside played with verve, and beautiful songs sung with that emotional commitment Jim brings to every performance. He sang 'The Wild Geese'. In its synthesis of Violet Jacob's fey poetry, the haunting tune, and the aching resonance achieved by Jim's voice, I still believe it to be one of the great Scottish songs of the 20th century.

Twenty years on, it is a privilege to contribute to this collection. I use the word deliberately, for like many in the Scots song tradition before him, the collection and enhancement of what is already there is as important as the creation of new songs. Indeed a sign of someone immersed in the tradition is that it is often difficult to detect where the old ends and the new begins – 'The Vinney Den' and 'Whar the Dichty Rins' are separated by a hundred years in their composition, but they are recognisably similar in language and tone, part of a distinctive cultural unity. Reading the book, it strikes me that Jim's strength comes from his ability to bridge different areas of Scottish life; he is a Dundonian with personal awareness of the urban experience, yet he has aye been at hame in the country; he is an East Coast Lowlander yet he has always drifted West to the hills abuin Angus and beyond to the mountains of Mull where his sympathy for Gaelic culture shines through; he is a skaldie who has earned the respect of the traivelin fowk through the kind of sensitivity he shows in the introduction to 'The Stewarts of Blair'; he is a singer revered among traditionalists, yet his band has long been a favourite among country dance aficionados, while his humorous compositions have a definite echo of the Music Hall.

Dipping into the book is like haein a guid crack wi an auld frien ower a few drams. The sangs and their introductions range over Jim's life as someone in tune with the whole of Scotland – his description of how he gets to a gig in Mull takes on epic proportions! But it is the deep love he has in particular for the gowden triangle of Angus formed by Letham, Auchmithie and Dundee that is the core of the book for me. There he is hilarious, angry, pawky, crabbit, couthy, thrawn, nostalgic and every ither emotion kennt by man. There is also an enduring humanity and sensibility at work in his awareness of the trials of his fellow creatures from auld friens dwinin, to disabled folk's suffering, to man's inhumanity to beasts like 'The Deein Stag'. It is the voice of a man of integrity, auld eneuch for wisdom and nostalgia, but young eneuch for a guid wheen year yet tae be "freewheelin down the brae".
Mary Brooksbank is richt, we're aw the better o' a sang, especially gin it's sung by a maister like Jim Reid.

BK
Newport-On-Tay

The Better o' a Sang

I've often had difficulty in accepting the title 'songwriter' even although I've written quite a few songs in my time. Its just that my picture of a songwriter is someone like George Gershwin sitting at his piano and the musical gems flowing with his conveyor belt regularity.

This is certainly not the case with me, probably because I've often had difficulty in accepting the title 'songwriter'. In other words, I think it's my attitude that's all wrong.

It's the same with my singing. Naturally I've always been 'over the moon' when I've had a good report in a newspaper or on the radio, but if someone comes up to me and says how marvellous a singer I am, I'm so embarrassed that I really don't know how to reply.

Music, in the early years of my life, was always on the sidelines, something like a substitute, never getting on the field of play until the last five minutes of the game. But the subconscious, it seems, took a lot of it on board and, at length, when this 'singing thing' took me over, I was able to remember songs that I didn't even know existed. An example of this is a song called The Foggy Foggy Dew, which I heard in a folk club around 1964, and I realised that I knew every word of it without knowing how. I can only surmise that there were so many songs crammed in at the time of Hogmanay that I forgot it all the next day only to remember 15 to 20 years later.

Since the early 1980s, I have been frequently asked why I haven't published a book of all my songs, especially 'The Wild Geese'. Well, this is it. These songs are part of a time and place which can never be recaptured except through their performance. I hope you will enjoy singing and playing these tunes.

Jim Reid
Letham, Angus

Song Titles

Starting out

The Better o' a Sang	13
The Foondry Band	14
The Foondry Bar	15
Grant Farquharson of Inveravon	16
Bella and Roy	17
Jim Reid of Letham	18
Fergie's Isla	19
The Isla Watcher	20
Stewarts of Blair	21
Auchmithie	22
Loch Duich	23
Rumness	24
Doonwind o' Bogheid	25
Auchmithie Cliffs	26
C. Stewart of North Lodge	27
The Auld Beech Tree	28
Craw Craw Heedrum Ha	29
Turin, Lour an' Lownie O'	30
The Taysiders	31
Adam's 'Loch Lomond'	32
Charlie's version – 'The Wedding o' McPhee'	33
The Bonnie Banks o' Loch Lomond	34
The Spark Amang the Heather	35
The 'Poli' Folly	36

Dundee

Eh'm Fae Dundee	41
Catherine Street	42
Whar the Dichty Rins	43
And We Didn't Know	44
The Stobbie Parliament Picnic	45
The Dixie Fu' o' Beans	46
The Vinney Den	47

Violet Jacob's poems

The Wild Geese	51
Rohallion	52
Faur-Ye-Weel	53/54
Tinkers Baloo	55
Halloween	56
The Wise Like Chap	57
The Greylag Geese	58
The Tramp to the Tattie-dulie	59

Friends and family

Back in Time	62
Marag Cnocach	63
Archie's Caravan	64
Expert Angler	65
The Deein' Stag	66
I Canna Find the Thyme	67
Freewheelin' Now	68
The Foundry Band	69
James and Dinah's Diamond Waltz	70
Welcome to the Glen	71
Back in Scotland	72
Another World	73
Linda A. Reid	74
Craig D. Reid	75
For the Love of My Country	76
Jamie Reid	77
The Laird o' Pitmuies	78
The Den o' Aldbar	79
Auld Ballumbie	80/81
Who Said 'The times Are a' Changin'	82
Stravaigin'	83

A great partnership

Isle of Mull	87
The Winds of Tiree	88
The Moothie Man	89
Fly Again	90
An Ordinary Genius	91

It's been fun

No Indispensable Man	95
The Road to Nowhere	96
We Span the Sea	97
The Constant Flow Pump	98
I Talk to the Trees	98
It Took You Long Enough	99
Three Words	100
Music on His Mind	101
The Guiding Lights	102
Scots Wha Hae	103
It's Been Fun	104

The Better o' a Sang

When Mary Brooksbank, Dundee Jute Worker, Trade Unionist, Poet, Songwriter, Author of the well-known 'O Dear Me' gave me her poem 'The Better o' a Sang' to set a tune to, I was 'over the moon'.

Our folk group at that time was 'The Shifters' and we sang Mary's song, 'O Dear Me' at every gig we played.

Reading her book made me realize that she must have had a wide knowledge of current affairs and politics. Aye, she wasna' jist a puir wee shifter.

This song gives us all some advice on how to cheer up when faced with big problems.

'The Better o' a Sang' CD and Cassette was published in 1996. I had planned for the book to be produced shortly after that but as Rabbie says, "The best laid plans o' mice and men gang aft agley."

What tho' the day be awfy lang
I'll aye get thro' it wi' a sang.
What tho' ma hert be o' sae sair
Tae hide the hurt I'll sing the mair.
What tho' I hae but litte gear
A wee bit sang will bring me cheer.
What tho' o' freens I hae but few
Tae them I'll sing for they are true.

What tho' I be sae awfy puir
A sang will banish a' ma care.
I sing nae sangs o' classic lore
O' Scotia's lilts I hae a score.
'Auld Robin Gray', 'The Rowan Tree'
memories dear, they're dear tae me.
Ma favourite when ma hert wis glad
'Whistle an I'll Come to You My Lad'.

Whatever fortune brings tae me
I'll sing a sang whar e'er I be.
There's naething that can daunt me lang
Gin I hae power tae sing a sang.
The sun, the birds, a flooer, a tree
They a' can wring a sang frae me.
Whatever may be richt or wrang
We're a' the better o' a sang.

The Foondry Band

I canna sing like Tannahill
Nor paint, like Scott, lake, mountain, rill
Nor climb fame's mount wi' Robin's skill
An' giant speed.
Yet I may make some fond heart thrill
Wi' my puir reed.

We canna play like Jimmy Shand
Nor fiddle the way that Skinner planned
Nor have we got the brilliant hand
O' auld Will Starr
But we're the famous Foondry Band.
Ye'll hae heard waur.

I found this verse by David Carnegie, a 19th century 'Reid Lichtie', and added the second verse.

In the sixties we were 'The Shifters' and our theme song was 'Oh Dear Me', the mill's gaen fest, the puir wee shifters canny get a rest'.

We werna' puir and we certainly werna' wee. But Mary Brooksbank liked us singin' her songs, and she approved of us using it as our theme song. I have altered one of her other poems and made a song of it which could easily become my present day theme song.

Folk all over the country often ask me if the band still plays in the Foundry Bar, Arbroath. The answer is that we, as a band, never really played there. It was a place, and still is, where any musician can turn up and join in the sessions. It was only when we played 'awa frae hame' that we were called 'The Foundry Band'.

The name started when we first won the ceilidh band competition at the Kinross Festival, and it's stuck ever since, even though the personnel changed a few times.

After that competition, the only one of its kind in Scotland at the time, the newspapers printed the story that we must be world ceilidh band champions.

Our popularity spread, and, with the making of our first record, we began to realise that we were bridging a gap between the folk music and the country dance band fraternities. At the festivals we would meet some of the great names in the traditional music scene and have the opportunity to play with them. I remember the great sense of elation when playing with Jimmy Shand. He always came to have a crack with me at concerts as he had known my father in his young days when he stayed in Dundee near our garage.

The wee pub, which we were catapulting into international fame, would have, I think, started off as one in a row of fishermen's cottages not far from the harbour. In our early days of playing it was owned by Dave Stott, and was just a man's pub with only one toilet, a real primitive one at that.

When Bella took over, the first thing that had to be done was 'bog renovation'. We said that was so the tourists could have before and after pictures.

The Foondry Bar

The Foondry Bar song was originally written by a local farmer who was a regular at the pub. I'll not tell you his name because he stole the tune from a singer you'll maybe know. On the song, which I recorded, I took the first two verses of the original and added the rest.

I'll leave you to guess the tune.

Oot alang Millgate and doon by the Broo
Ye'll find a wee door that was welcoming you
Whar ye got the best service in Arbroath, by far
When ye met Davie Stott o' the Foondry Bar.

Foondry Bar, the reek rolling doon tae the sea
My desire wis always tae be near
The Foondry Bar

The furnishing's lavish expense didnae lack
When ye went tae the bog ye'd tae turn yer back.
There's darts and there's dominos, best onywhar
The nightlife o' Arbroath, the Foondry Bar.

Chorus

But the pub was ta'en ower by Bella and Roy
An' the bog renovations made peein' a joy.
There's a place for a woman noo, and ane for a man
An' ye jist ca' the han'le tae flush oot the pan.

Chorus

An' when Bella took ower then a'body kent
Whit 'These are my mountains' actually meant.
When closing time cam' nae bell you could hear
She jist gave a birl an' the hale place was clear.

Chorus

But whit maks the Foondry abune a' the rest
The musical evenin's the finest and best
So pit on yer coat we'll go doon for a jar
An' a tune or a sang at the Foondry Bar.

Chorus

Grant Farquharson of Inveravon Chae Geddes

Chae Geddes (centre) was the man who made the Foundry magic for me. His fiddle fairly drove us along, his face beaming, and the crack was always brilliant when he was around. Things have never been quite the same since his death.

Here's three of his tunes.

Bella and Roy
Chae Geddes

Jim Reid of Letham
Chae Geddes

Fergie's Isla

Tonight he covers the risin' troot
That rings the flet 'alow the hawthorn's shade
Wi' nymph and spinner o' olive licht an' dark
He's tried afore wi' nae offer made.

But tonight the wind is in the west,
An' the sun is lost in a passin' cloud,
An' Isla's water is clear and fresh,
A million miles from the city's crowd.

Upstream the fallin' white foam roars,
By the crum'lin' grey-walled mill,
Wi' leakin' raifs an creakin' flairs,
An' big wheel lyin' sadly still.

Swiftly arcs his flee an' saftly draps.
His hand, his een, his mind are one.
Up comes the troot, he strikes and hopes
Wi' poundin' hert as he lets it run.

The reel screams, the rod bends, his hand gropes for the net,
An' the pool is now a turbulent foam,
But its losin' it's strength, as he reels in the line,
At last he's lured his auld prey from its home.

Wi' the troot in his bag he relaxes once more,
And his thochts turn tae different things,
O' the country by 'Rivven' he'll always adore,
An' the peace o' mind fair Isla brings.

Whenever I hear the name 'Fergie' mentioned, its not a topless royal or even a Man' U boss that comes to mind. I recall a time when I was in my twenties and my 'Fergie' was in his late forties or early fifties. He was my fishing companion and unconscious adviser on 'a' things country'. He had a cabin on the banks of the Isla at Ruthven and we spent many a happy time there. He had an attitude towards angling and, perhaps, life in general that took me a long time to understand, if I ever did.

One day we were fishing in a competition and the trout had been particularly 'dour'. Fergie was lying up the bank when a 'great rise' came on. I gave him a shout, which wakened him up. He took out his pipe and began to light it, saying, "I've waited for them a' day, now its their turn tae wait for me".

While most of us weighed in catches of three, four, or five fish, Fergie won the contest with just one, a whopper of over four pounds.

He never had casts all made up ready to change, like the rest of us, and he kept his flies in his tobacco tin. One night, on Lintrathen Loch, he decided to change a fly. The fish were quite lively and he seemed to be taking a long time about it. I shouted up the boat "What's up?" he shouted back "I've shairly smoked thon bloody butcher".

This is the first poem I ever wrote. It was published in the *Strathmore Angling Association Handbook* of 1965.

The Isla Watcher

After the worldwide acclaim of the 1965 edition of the Strathmore Angling Handbook the committee asked me to write another poem for the 1966 edition. "Wait a minute," I said "I'm no' a poet. That was just a flash in the pan". Anyway I thought about it and decided to do one for Tom Johnstone, the river watcher – a man disliked by most anglers because most anglers will resort to bending the rules provided nobody sees them. Tom was the man most likely to see them. He had the knack of turning up just when you had decided to do something which was not quite legal, and he was not reluctant to exercise his authority. However, I remember being told how little he got paid for the job and thinking that he must love it. So I wrote this poem for him, "after all he wisnae a bad lad tae hae a crack wi' as lang as he didnae see that tin o' maggots in yer pocket".

Why does he do it folk wonder, why
There must be a reason they say
But it isn't for money, there's little of that
No you wouldn't go far for his pay.

But he doesn't desire to go very far
And the favours he asks for are few
Just as long as his legs stay as strong as they are
And his eyes can still take in the view.

Just as long as the view is the Isla he loves
He'll continue to watch o'er its banks
And when he sees an angler enjoying his sport
It's as if he was hearing "Tom, thanks."

Dear Madam I'm calling your district to-day,
When you pick up my card please don't throw it away,
Just you sit down and read it, you never can tell,
You may have some old junk that you want to sell.

Perhaps a hair mattress or maybe some brass,
For old stuff like that is far better in cash;
You may have some jewellery you no longer like
Or a second-hand car or your husband's old bike.

Your old rags or woollens are of no further use,
I am sure they are far better oot o' the hoose;
Then your old cast-off clothing—yer ain or the man's,
Your auld iron pots or your brass jelly pans.

They're the things that I'm efter, just tae mention a few,
So get up and get busy—gie the hoose a guid do,
And you'll no' be sorry when I call tae collect,
I'm the first honest dealer that you've ever met.

————————

STEWART, BLAIRGOWRIE

Belle Stewart told me many stories of her life, and so engrossing they have all been. She showed me the spot where she was born, in a bow tent, on the banks of the Tay near Dunkeld. But her father died when she was very young and her mother had to 'settle' according to the rules of the travellers.

When she married Alex, she had to help him with his business, which was hawking between Blairgowrie, Dunkeld and Pitlochry. She told me she felt a little self-conscious about knocking on doors for the first time, so she wrote a poem and had it printed on a card and put it through all the letter boxes. Then she knocked on the doors the week after, and the results were amazing. The customers had all their stuff ready and waiting for her return.

She gave me one of the original cards, and I've treasured it for years. Here is a copy of it.

Stewarts of Blair

Alex Stewart picked up my pipes and started to blow, gave a drone a bit of a twist, then played a couple of tunes. His wife Belle had a worried look all through his performance. Why did the crowd cheer like mad when he stopped? He'd played better than that before. The answer is that the crowd knew he was not a well man, in fact he was dying, and he knew it. He had never played for a long time and he knew that this would be his last time. He handed me back my pipes and I could see the tears in his eyes.

I wrote this tune in honour of a family who will always be part of me.

Auchmithie

There's a wee fishing village on the shores of the North Sea.
Once famous for smoked haddock, and they ca'd it Auchmithie.
I don't know where this name came from, or what it really means,
But once ye know Auchmithie, ye'll see it in your dreams.

It was there that I wis born, many, many years ago,
In a wee old stone cottage, overlooking the round-o.
Wi' the cliffs sae high and rugged, washed by wild seas from below,
Such a place ye will ne'er see, no matter where ye go.

For I've been around Loch Lomond, and Tobermory Bay,
Inverary and Loch Fyne, and all along the way,
But the bonniest spot that I've seen, and aye will be tae me,
Is the rocks and cliffs and green braes o' my dear home Auchmithie.

A poem by an exile, which I set to music, had become Auchmithie's anthem. Norman Buick, whose family emigrated to Canada when he was just a boy, never forgot his native village and visited it regularly in his old age.

Loch Duich

I'll give you another of Belle's compositions, which she put to the pipe tune of Loch Duich, but the story is taking place in Glencoe, a favourite haunt of Alex and his pipes.

Belle herself has now passed away and hopefully the Loch Duich last verse has come to pass.

Her daughter, Sheila, is doing a marvellous job of keeping their family traditions alive.

As I was walking with my lover
Down a glen that was so fair,
There I heard a piper playing,
And his music filled the air.

As I listened to the music,
And it sounded loud and clear,
I sat down among the heather
Wi' the lass that I love dear.

The tune he played it was 'Loch Duich'
That's a grand old Scottish air,
There I woo'd and won my lassie,
Amang the heather blooming fair.

All my friends are widely scattered,
Some I'll never see again,
Others they have left their homeland
For to sail across the main.

But I hope we'll be together,
As we were so long ago,
When I heard that piper playing,
In the valley of Glencoe.

Rumness

Rumness is a place o' wild scenic grandeur,
Whar the rocks change the water tae white roarin' foam,
Whar the wind forces a'thing tae bend tae its power,
But abune a'thing else Rumness is my home.

Rumness is a place whaur the seabirds a' gather,
Whar the herring-gull, puffin and guillemot roam,
Whar the fulmar soars high, in the bright breezy weather
A' the birds are my neighbours, Rumness is oor home.

Rumness is a place that stands right on the edge,
Whar the land tak's a plunge strecht doon tae the sea,
Whar the kittiwakes nest on the narrowest ledge,
Jist like the seabirds, Rumness is for me.

When I sit at my door an' I view a' the beauty,
I'll thank him abune us an' ask him tae bless
The kind fowk o' Auchmithie, wha gied me their freendship,
An' showed me the road that leads ower tae Rumness.

When I left Dundee, I got a place along the cliffs from Auchmithie called Rumness. It was a converted wartime lookout and gun position. I loved it there, but vandals wouldn't leave it alone, and I was spending most of my time repairing broken windows. However, I did find enough time to write a couple of songs. The first one I hardly ever performed. Its called *Rumness*. The second, *Doon-wind o' Bogheid,* I recorded and it's become quite popular with the locals.

The 'kind fowk' in the last verse were, in particular, the late Florie Cargill and her husband George.

Doonwind o' Bogheid

Ken Grant of the fourth verse, ran the family farm by Auchmithie but quite a few years ago he left it and moved to Glen Isla. I wonder if the famous Bogheid air got the better of him.

And one wee poem.

Frae Lunan Bay tae Dickmont Law,
Just gie yer nose the lead,
It'll aye tak' ye the quickest way
Tae the ferm they ca' Bogheid

Doonwind o' Bogheid
Ye'll wish that ye were deid
Ye can plainly tell by the helluva smell
Ye're doonwind o' Bogheid.

Bogheid has a piggery
Weel kent the country roon'
For the wind near shook it tae the grund
In Lindsey Ross's tune

Chorus

Now Ethie castle's a gey braw place,
A stately home indeed,
But ye widna want tae bide there lang,
When ye're doonwind o' Bogheid.

Chorus

Ken Grant will trudge thro' sleat an' snaw
Tae gie his coos their feed,
But the puir beasts will jist hiv tae stairve
When they're doonwind o' Bogheid

Chorus

But ye ken the farmworkers,
They're a tough an' hardy breed,
They never have a cough or cauld,
When they're working at Bogheid.

Doonwind o' Bogheid
Ye'll wish that ye were deid
Ye can plainly tell by the helluva smell
Ye're doonwind o' Bogheid.

Auchmithie Cliffs

A calm and sunny day
I viewed the cliffs
And wondered how
The wind and waves
Could carve so many
Holes and grooves
And pinnacles
And caves

A wild and stormy day
I viewed the cliffs
And wondered in
That fearsome squall
How there could be
A cliff
Left there at all.

C. Stewart of North Lodge

Then I met Christine Stewart whom I'd known as a brilliant folk-singer in the '60's. I wrote this pipe tune for her.

The Auld Beech Tree

In a field by the pond an auld beech tree stood
An' each day as we walked up the track
We aye stopped tae gaze at its beautiful form,
Never left it without glancin' back.

It must've stood there for hundreds of years
An' its limbs were as big as maist trees.
It had seen a few autumns an' summers an' springs
An' mony a cauld winter's breeze.

'Till yon nicht o' the storm that raged thro' the land
Causin' havoc in country an' toon
An' when we gaed up by the pond the next day
We saw that the auld tree wis doon.

We jist stood and stared for speech widna' come
It wis jist like the death o' a freen,
When I turned tae Christine wi' a lump in ma throat
I could see she had tears in her een.

But ye ken whit they say aboot an ill wind
That blaws, but does somebody good,
The winter can blaw, wi' its frost an' its snaw
Aye but oor fire winna gang oot.

I overcame my sadness at the loss of one of Nature's beautiful giants with some chain-saw therapy.

Craw Craw Heedrum Ha

And one of Nature's fly men gets the
last laugh on me.

There's thistles and nettles and dokens and wrack,
Ma spade's wearin' dune aye and likewise ma back
An' thon bluidy craw he jist sits in the tree
An' a' the day lang he is laughin at me.
Craw craw heedarum ha

Some say that derision is no his intent
When he sits there an' craws a' the time my back's bent
Wi' swingin' the scythe for tae cut the lang grass,
I dinna believe that he's crawin' for a lass.
Craw craw heedarum ha

Ye'll no see 'm for miles if ye come wi' a gun,
His instinct aye tells him tae be on the run.
But workin' the clatt 'till yer shithers are sair
Is certain tae start him aff laughin' ance mair.
Craw craw heedarum ha

It's a fact that the cleverest being is man,
He reigns so supreme within Nature's great plan.
But sometimes I think we micht hae it a' wrang
When I think o' the craw laughin' a' the day lang.
Craw craw heedarum ha
Craw craw heedarum ha

Turin, Lour an' Lownie O'

Chorus
Dunichen and Guthrie
Lour and Turin
They're the hills
Aroond aboot Letham
Carmyllie Fother'n'ham Dumbarra'
Turin Lour an' Lownie O'

The Fithy Wid, an the Wuddy Law, man
Braikie, Hatton Mill and Friock, man
I spiered at a man I'm lookin' for Letham
He says ye'r daein' fine man hud even on.

Look for - Dunichen etc.

Then I asked the wye frae a lad an' a lass, man
He said left an' she said richt, man
I thocht I'd slip awa afore it cam tae blows, man
An I thocht o' the hills then held even on.

Look for – Dunichen etc.

Well I passed Milldens an' turned up a brae, man
An' stopped at a corner an looked a' around, man
An' when I saw the hills, I knew there was Letham
For the mannie had tell't me tae hud even on.

There was – Dunichen etc.

The Taysiders

Jim Ramsay

In my early days of playing at the Foundry Bar, I was still a member of the Dundee folk group called 'The Taysiders'. Jim Ramsay, one of the Foundry regular fiddlers at that time, wrote this jig for us. He was an excellent composer, with many fine tunes to his credit.

Adam's 'Loch Lomond'

It was ae summer's nicht that I got an awfu' fricht
When I went for a swim in Loch Lomond
An I fund when I cam oot that ma claes were nae aboot
Some passer-by had pinched them in the gloamin'.
So I couldna tak' the high road, I couldna tak' the low road,
Roond aboot the banks I gaed roamin'.
I wis sic an afae sicht until the broad daylicht,
I wis cerried hame in blankets frae Loch Lomond

Noo I went on a spree at a local jubilee
In a hoose on the banks o' Loch Lomond
An' I very near got hung for a song that I had sung
An' they threatened they wid droon me in Loch Lomond.
For I couldna get the high notes I couldna hit the low notes,
The maister o' the hoose he wis foamin'.
An' I clean forgot the air when they hit me wi' a chair
An' they chased me roond the banks o' Loch Lomond.

Now a big surprise I got when I went oot in a boat
On a fishin' expedition on Loch Lomond
An' I hooked a muckle wecht an' I'm gonna tell ye strecht,
It took me a' that nicht until next mornin'.
For it widna tak the high road it widna tak the low road,
The beast wis ower a ton I wis foamin'
An' whit dae ye think I seen smilin' thro' two eyes of green,
'Twas the Loch Ness monster in Loch Lomond.

So I had a drink or twa before I gaed awa
In a hotel on the banks o' Loch Lomond
An' I fair enjoyed masel' 'till they rang the closin' bell
Then I lay doon on the banks of Loch Lomond.
For I couldna see the high road I couldna see the low road
As I lay paralysed in the gloamin'.
Next mornin' wi' a drouth an' I'm tellin' you the truth,
I drank a power o' water frae Loch Lomond.

The Taysiders were Jim Craig, Ken McKay and myself. We used to do a lot of ceilidhs throughout Angus and into Perthshire, along with two pals in song, Charlie Murray and Adam Young. These two could fairly liven up a ceilidh. At one particular session a wisecracker bet us we didn't know 'Loch Lomond'. Well, I sang the popular version, Adam sang his version, Charlie sang his, and I finished it off with what I believe to be the oldest version. This wisecracker didn't open his mouth again. You won't be needing the tune or the words of the famous song, but here are the other three. The tune is the same on them all.

Charlie's version - 'The Wedding o' McPhee'

At mony sprees I've been but the best ane I have seen
It was held high up on Ben Lomond.
Near everyone was fu' it was like a Waterloo.
'Twas the weddin' o' McPhee on Ben Lomond.
For some came up the high road and some came up the low road,
Some of them got lost in the gloamin'
And them that bade awa, they wer'na there ava',
At the weddin' o' McPhee on Ben Lomond.

The Minister he got lost we searched for him of course.
We searched round the banks o' Loch Lomond,
But we found him on the hill, in his hand he held a gill
At the weddin' o' McPhee on Ben Lomond.
So they kicked him up the high road they kicked him up the low road,
Somebody kicked his abdomen
And afore he went awa' he wished he'd never saw
The weddin' o' McPhee on Ben Lomond.

Then we had a feed we had pies and potted heid.
There was bannocks stacked high in the gloamin'.
The rump o' a coo, the leg o' a cushie doo
At the weddin' o' McPhee on Ben Lomond.
Then some gaed hame the high road and some gaed hame the low road
An' some of them got lost in the gloamin',
But the bridegroom and the bride were cremated side by side
At the weddin' o' McPhee on Ben Lomond.

The Bonnie Banks o' Loch Lomond

Oh whither away my bonnie bonnie May
So late and so far in the gloamin'.
The mist gathers grey over muirland and brae.
Oh whither alane art thou roamin'.

I trysted my ain love the night in the broom,
My Ranald wha lo'es me sae dearly,
For the morrow he marches to Edinburgh toun
To fecht for the king and Prince Charlie.

Yet why weep ye sae my bonnie bonnie May.
Yer true love from battle returning.
Yer darlin' will claim in the micht o' his fame
An' change into gladness your mourning.

Oh weel may I weep yestreen in my sleep
We stood bride and bridegroom thegither,
But his lips and his breath were as chilly as death
An' his heart's bluid lay red on the heather.

Oh dauntless in battle as tender in love,
He'll yield ne'er a fit tae the foeman.
But never again frae the field o' the slain
To Moira he'll come in the gloamin'.

Oh he'll gang the high road an' I'll gang the low.
But I'll be in heaven afore him,
For my bed is prepared in the mossy graveyard
'Mang the hazels o' green Inverarnan.

The thistle shall bloom and the king hae his ain
And fond lovers meet in the gloamin'
And me an' my true love will yet meet again
Far abune the bonnie banks o' Loch Lomond.

This version I got from Ford's Vagabond Songs.

I believe this version was written by the same person who wrote the famous song and that her name was Lady John Scott.

The Spark Amang the Heather

I wrote this song after reading a book about John McPherson, the man who instigated the formation of 'The Land League', which, eventually, was successful in getting the clearances abolished.

When they brought us all together,
Told us that we had to go
Leave our homes that we were born in,
Leave the only life we know.

We were poor but honest crofters
Working hard so we might stay
On the land our fathers gave us,
Ne'er thought we'd be forced away.

We replied we'll never leave home,
Never set sail o'er the sea.
Let the police come and the soldiers
To leave home we won't agree.

Others have been put on board ships,
Sailed away out o'er the deep.
Then the landlords burned their houses
To make way for flocks of sheep.

Then along came John McPherson,
Humble crofter from Glendale
Held a meeting formed a land league,
For his efforts thrown in jail

But the spark amang the heather
Soon became a burning flame
And the highlanders united
Vowed they'd never leave their hame.

But the glens still show the scars
Of these evictions of before
And the shells of empty houses
Echo laughter sounds no more.

The 'Poli' Folly

You can speak about that bold and glorious pirate Captain Kidd
Of the galleons that he captured and treasures that he hid.
You can tell me of treasures deep in Tobermory Bay.
But there isn't any treasure like the one sunk at Calvay.

It was on that February night in 1941
When *The Politician* ran aground and started all the fun.
There were men from Oban, Stornoway, Rhum, Barra, Eigg and Coll
And the whisky flowed like water with enough to drown us all.

Well we put to sea in every sort of boat that we could pinch.
There were cobbles with their drunken crews all scattered o'er the Minch
And when we landed safely drinking whisky just like beer
We had a more hilarious time than many a New Year.

But the Customs men arrived and they said they had to search the croft.
They lifted up the floor boards and raked all through the loft.
But they didn't try the peat stack or in the horse's hay,
Nor did they find the bottles buried all along the bay.

If you're ever on our island walking on the silver strand
And you chance to see a shiny object peeping through the sand.
Just have a go at digging a surprise perhaps you'll get
For half the stuff we hid so well we haven't found it yet.

Recite this poem using your 'Parahandy' type Highland accent.

Eh'm Fae Dundee

However, eh'm fae Dundee. This is a humorous look at the differences in our speech. When one spoke with a strong dialect in Dundee one was liable to overhear the comment – 'Dyihearum. Eee's that oary ee op'ns ees mooth an' a bale o' jait fa's oot'.

Of course there are not many bales of jute left in Dundee nowadays.

Noo Stornoway's no whar eh'm fae Lochmaddy nor Portree
When the bale o' jait fa's oot ma mooth ye'll ken eh'm fae Dundee.

I went to a Highland ceilidh once and gave them all a song,
the fear an tighe was keen to know what island I belong.

Chorus

The teuchters all looked puzzled as I stood in kilt and sporran
And spluttered out a port a puel and sang about Ben Dorain.

Chorus

I've sung aboot young Colin's crow or the dubh that flew in Moulin
Or the sheeny van whas fan belt broke in the middle of the Cuilin.

Chorus

I love the Highlands every bit from Caithness to Tiree,
But I wish they'd learn tae a' speak richt, ken, the wey like in Dundee.

Chorus

Catherine Street

Ae day I wandered all alane
Ma thochts contrived tae mak' me greet.
It was on a wee bit skelp o' grund
That aince wis kent as Catherine Street.

The demolition squad's been there
An' every stick and stane they've cleared.
They said the hooses wernae fit
For modern families tae be reared.

I suppose I must agree wi' them
The conveniences I'd say were bad,
But the fowk in thae auld days lang syne
Fair made the maist o' whit they had.

An' as I lingered there a while
My sadness slowly turned to joy
When mindin' o' the pals I had
An' the games we played when jist a boy.

At pinner, or tig, or kick the can,
Or closey headers an a' the rest,
Or at the fitba' in the street,
The Caithy lads could beat the best.

Then we'd slip in tae Mrs Pike's,
That's if we'd money tae oor name
An' a penny Vantass we wid buy
Tae refresh us for another game.

In the march of time a' things must change
A' for the best or so they say.
But sometimes I think it wid be braw
If the clock could go back for jist a day.

I was sitting in the car park off Dura Street, eating a Wallace's 'peh' and looking around me trying to visualise this street of tenements, where I played as a boy, when the song just came to me. I picked up a pen and wrote it down on the empty 'peh' bag.

Whar the Dichty Rins

I put a tune to a poem written in the
nineteenth century by James Lowe,
a Dundonian poet and fiddler.
The song reminds me of all the pals
I had, especially a lass called
Muriel Anderson.

Whar the Dichty Rins by yon fairy dell,
Whar the rowan tree hings abune the well,
Though there's nae cascades, falls or roarin' linns,
Yet there's beauty spots where Dichty rins.

Whar the Dichty Rins by yon hawthorn tree,
There I first met ane dearest still tae me,
Ilka neuk we kent a' its oots an' ins,
Lovingly we strayed whar the Dichty rins.

Whar the Dichty rins near yon auld Mains den
Bairnies blithely play a' the games they ken.
When, at nicht, the moon keeks doon atween the whins
Lovers fondly stray whar the Dichty rins.

Whar the Dichty rins o' I fain would be
There's nae ither burn half sae dear tae me.
When I wi' auld age totter on ma pins
I'll haud hame tae dee, whar the Dichty rins.

And We Didn't Know

I was born in the city at the mouth of the Tay
When the big ships came in to the harbour each day
And the smell of the jute filled the air
And the noise of the looms everywhere.

And the bummer would blow
And the women would go
And we didn't know
That the men were away to the war.

Every day after school we'd go out to the street
With the rest of our pals who we'd promised to meet
And we booted a ball 'til it burst,
To us nothing could ever be worse.

And the bummer would blow
And the women would go
And we didn't know
That the men were away to the war.

And sometimes a siren would sound through the night,
In the shelter we'd play 'til the bombers took flight
And we wondered how ma looked worn out
When the chapper-up gave her a shout.

And the bummer would blow
And the women would go
And we didn't know
That the men were away to the war.

Now all of that seems such a long time ago.
I'm a stranger to this town that I used to know
Where the smell of the jute filled the air
There's no noise of the looms anywhere.

And the bummer would blow
And the women would go
And we didn't know
That the men were away to the war.

Thinking back again to my schoolboy days during the war, I start to realise how lucky we were. Streets were like playgrounds, there was so little traffic on them. We played football, rounders, cricket, and hide-and-seek on them. We cycled, sledged, and drove pilers on even the main streets.

The adults of that time had a hard and worried life but they kept it all from us kids. In the words of this song – we didn't know.

The Stobbie Parliament Picnic

My grandfather, Jamie Reid, ran the Maryfield Stables in Dundee, and with the passing of time and of the horse, the stables became Maryfield Garage, run by my dad and his two brothers (the 'twinnies'). But the old lads still 'stabled' their cars there, and, when I was a schoolboy, there was always a crowd gathered at the garage in the evening, and the talk was mostly horses. My grandfather had lost a hand in an accident, so he figured prominently in the stories of horsemanship and daring.

This poem was featured in the *Maryfield Gazette* in 1908. The 'auld men's club' meetings at the shelter in the middle of the Stobswell junction continued until at least the 50s.

In the shelter o' the shelter at the top of Albert Street,
There's a sturdy crowd of veterans who regularly meet;
Discuss the situation in a house of common style,
An' they hech an' they pech an' they haver an' they're happy a' the while.
Wi' ma fal lal lal di ma ral di dal, Ma fal lal lal di day.

Ae day while hot debate was on, Jamie Reid cam near,
"I think we'll organise a drive while summer days are here."
The auld lads said it wad be great the countryside tae see,
Says Jamie, "I'll get oot the brake, just leave it up tae me."
Wi' ma fal lal lal di ma ral di dal, Ma fal lal lal di day.

The plan was soon adopted and arrangements duly made,
Whereby the outin' wad take place and a' expenses paid.
There was fellowship and freedom and refreshments beyond praise.
Twas the rarest and the fairest and the merriest of days.
Wi' ma fal lal lal di ma ral di dal, Ma fal lal lal di day.

He drove the brake tae Tullybaccart and Kinclaven Bridge,
Whaur they had a marvellous picnic on dismounting from the rig.
The weather was sae kind to them, the sun shone a' the while.
The return journey took them roon' by Meigle and Newtyle.
Wi' ma fal lal lal di ma ral di dal, Ma fal lal lal di day.

So came a' ye that's gaithered here tae welcome them a' hame,
This trip has gained itself a place in Stobbie's hall of fame;
An' while ye're cheering ane an' a' just let me hear your cries
Of thanks for Jamie Reid's horse brake and Durkie's tasty pies.
Wi' ma fal lal lal di ma ral di dal, Ma fal lal lal di day.

The Dixie Fu' o' Beans

When we were only laddies
Jist new started in oor teens
Oor pride and joy wis push bikes.
Yon light weight tourin' machines
Wi' low slung alloy handle bars
An' saddles ower high
We'd bike ower a' the countryside
In weather weet or dry.

Tae Killiecrankie, Amulree,
Loch Rannoch, and Loch Tay,
The Devil's Elbow, Cairn o' Mount,
We pedalled a' the way.
Aince tourin' up aroond Speyside
We thocht on something new,
Took up the bikes and cerried them
Across the Lairig Ghru

We had oor favourite biley ups,
The Dochart at Killin,
The Hermitage, The Rum'lin' Brig,
The Tap o' Reekie Lynn.
At these rare spots we stopped tae crack
Wi' lads frae ither toons,
And sat around the primus stove,
Wi' mouthies, playin' tunes.

'Hurree horo fur scabbie Joe',
'Kate Bairdie had a coo',
An we a' gied it laldy then,
Eh ken the titles noo.
These places a' seem nearer now
We go by different means,
But oh the hiss o' primus stove
An' the Dixie fu' of beans.

I was fourteen. I wanted a bike capable of touring the country, camping and hostelling. Some pals had beautiful new ones that you could lift with your little finger. My dad told me that there were plenty of bits and pieces in the scrap heap at the back of the garage and I could build one for myself. I envied their new bikes for a while, but I soon came to realise that I knew every bit of my bike, having fitted it all together myself, and breakdowns were less frequent with my bike than some of the new ones. With it I covered an amazing amount of miles.

I named this song *The Dixie Fu' o' Beans*. Maybe it should be *O' for the Legs I Used to Have*.

The Vinney Den

Bowrie Fa'd, Bract'ly Brig, Vinney Den, Lownie, names just crying out to a Scottish poet. My effort received great praise from the highest source in the land – Hamish Henderson.

As I cam ower by Brackley Brig,
Twas on my way tae Bowrie Fa'd
I met wi sic a bonnie lass
Wad turn the heid o' ony lad.

Said I, "Ma dear it's getting' late,
The sun's lang drapped ower Lownie Hill,
Have you got very far to go?"
She said, "I bide at Idvies Mill."

"My faither he's the miller there,
An honest man ye'll shairly ken
He'll treat ye fairly if ye'll see
Me safely through the Vinney Den."

I took her hand and we set aff
Tae struggle doon the burnside.
The lengthening shadows grew sae dark,
My growin' fear I tried tae hide.

I said tae her,"Let's sing a sang
The tune will help us on our way."
She sang sae sweet I lost my fear
She fairly stole ma hert away.

But when we came tae the Feuars' Inn
Efter we'd won through dark Vinney Den
Ma bonnie lass was ta'en awa
By four and twenty angry men.

But she broke loose, cam rinnin' back
When she saw they'd tied me tae a tree
Sayin', "Is this the thanks a laddie gets
For a' the help he's been tae me."

They listened to her story then
They took a knife and cut me loose,
They set us baith upon a horse
And led us tae her faither's hoose.

Her faither was sae glad tae see
That she was safe and free from harm
And I was asked if I wad fee
As horseman at Auchterlownie fairm.

I coorted her from that day on
An' tae wed me she did agree.
Tho' auld an' grey we aye will mind
When she cam through the Vinney Den wi' me.

Poems by Violet Jacob

There couldn't be a book of my songs without acknowledging one of Scotland's greatest poets, Violet Jacob.

Born in 1863, she was an heiress to the House of Dun, near Montrose. Her maiden name was Kennedy-Erskine, but she had a way with the old Scots language, which convinces me that she must have used it every day as her 'first tongue'.

In a poem to her dead son, Harry killed in the 1914-18 war, she proves her love of it:

> 'Angus held you in her spell
> Her Grampians faint and blue
> Her ways, the speech you knew so well
> Were half the world to you.'

The next six songs are poems by Violet Jacob. Once I started reading her poems, some of them seemed to me to be 'natural songs'. The first poem I wrote a tune to was Rohallion and then The Wild Geese followed.

I hope I have done her poems justice with my tunes. I know that for a number of years now I have rekindled an interest in her poetry.

The Wild Geese

words Violet Jacob

O tell me fit was on yer road ye roarin' Norland Wind,
As ye come blawin' frae the land that's never frae ma mind.
Ma feet thay traivel England but I'm deein' for the north.
"Ma man I saw the siller tides run up the Firth o' Forth."

Aye wind I ken them weel eneuch and find they fall and rise
And fain I'd feel the creepin' mist on yonder shore that lies
But tell me as ye pass them by fit saw ye on the way.
"Ma man I rocked the rovin' gulls that sail abane the Tay."

But saw ye naethin' leein' wind afore ye cam tae Fife
For there's muckle lyin' ayont the Tay that's mair tae me nor life.
"Ma man I swept the Angus braes that ye hivna trod for years."
O wind forgie a hameless loon that canna see for tears.

"And far abune the Angus straths I saw the wild geese flee
A lang, lang skein o' beatin' wings wi' their heids toward the sea.
And aye their cryin' voices trailed ahint them on the air."
O wind hae mercy haud yer wheesht for a daurna listen mair.

Rohallion

words Violet Jacob

Ma buits are at rest on the midden,
I havenae a plack;
And ma breeks they're no dandy anes, forrit,
And they're waur at the back;
On the road that comes oot o' the Hielands
I see as I trayvel the airth
Frae the braes et the back o' Rohallion
The reek abane Perth.

There's a canny wee hoose wi' a gairden
In a neuk o' Strathtay;
An ma mither is bakin' the bannocks,
And the bairns are at play;
In the gloamin' ma faither, the shepherd,
Looks doon for a blink o' the licht
As he gathers the yowes at the sheiling
Tae fauld them at nicht.

Noo there isnae a hoose that could haud me
Frae here tae the sea
When a wind frae the braes o' Rohallion
Comes creepin' tae me;
And niver a lowe frae the ingle
Can draw like the trail an' the shine
O' the stars i' the loch o' Rohallion
A fitstep o' mine.

Noo the snaw's in the wind, an' the weepies
Hang deid on the shaw,
An' pale the leaves left on the rowan,
I'm soothward awa';
But a voice like a wraith blaws ahent me
And sings as I'm liftin' ma pack,
"I am waitin' – Rohallion, Rohallion –
Ma lad, ye'll be back!"

Faur-Ye-Weel

words Violet Jacob

As ye come through the Sea-gate ye'll find a hoose we ken
Whaur, when a man is drouthy, his drouth an' he gang ben,
And whiles o' nichts there's dancin' and aye there's drink by day
And a fiddler-carle sits yonder an' gars his fiddle play.
Oh come, ye ancient mariners
Nae matter soond or lame,
For tho' ye gae on hirplin' tae
Ye'll syne gang dancin' hame.
The years are slippin' past ye
Like water past the bows
Roond half the warld ye've tossed yer dram
But soon ye'll Hae to lowse!

Faur-Ye-Weel (cont.)

The toon is like a picture, the sea is bonnie blue,
The fiddle's cryin' all the shore to captain, mate an' crew
An' them that's had for music the swirl o' gannets' wings,
The winds that drive frae Denmark, they dootna what it sings.
Oh come ye dandy Baltic lads
That sail to Elsinore.
Ye're newly in, ye'll surely win
To hae a spree ashore.
Lairn frae the sea yer maister,
When fortune's i' yer debt,
The cauld waves washin' past the bar
Tak a' that they can get!

And when the quays are lichtit an' dark the ocean lies,
The daft mune, like a feckless fule, keeks doon tae mock the wise,
Awa' in quiet closes the fiddles's voice is heard
Whaur some that should be sleepin' are listenin' for its word.
Sae haste ye now ye rovin' qheyns,
An gie yer dads the slip,
Tho' dour auld min sit girnin' ben
There's young anes aff the ship,
Come, take yer fill o' dancin',
Yer hert's at hame maun bide,
For the lad that tak's a he'rt to sea
Will drap it ower the side!

And aye the fiddle's playin', the auld bow wauks the string,
The carle, stampin' wi' his fit, gies aye the tune a swing.
Gang east, gang west, ye'll hear it, it lifts ye like a reel.
It's never dumb an' the tune sings "Come"
But its name is faur-ye-weel!

Tinkers Baloo

words Violet Jacob

Haud yer whisht, my mannie,
Hide yer heid the noo,
There's a jimp young mune i' the branches abune
An' she's keekin' at me an' you.
Near she is to settin'
Waukin she shouldna be,
An mebbe she sees i' the loan by the trees
Ower muckle far you an' me.

Dinna cry on daddie,
Daddie's by the fairm,
There's a speckie hen that strays i' the den
An ' he's fear'd she may come tae hairm.
Thieves is bauld an' mony,
That's what guid fowk say,
An' they'd a' complain gin the limmer was ta'en
An cheughit afore its day.

Sleep, an' then, come Saubath
A feather o' gray ye'll get
Wi' specklies on it to set in yer bonnet
An' gar ye look brawer yet.
Sae hide yer heid, my mannie,
Haud yer whisht, my doo,
For we'll hae to shift or the sun's i' the lift
An' I'm singin' Baloo, Baloo

Halloween

words Violet Jacob

The tattie liftin's nearly through,
They're ploughin' whaur the barley grew,
And aifter dark roond ilka stack,
Ye'll see the horsemen stand an' crack
O' Lachlan, but I mind o' you.

I mind foo often we hae seen
Ten thoosand stars keek doon atween
The naikit branches an' below
Baith fairm an' bothie hae their show,
Alowe wi' lichts o' Hallowe'en.

There's bairns wi' guisards at their tail
Clourin' the doors wi' runts o' kail,
And fine ye'll hear the skreich an' skirls
O' lassies wi' their droukit curls
Bobbin' for aipples i' the pail.

The bothie fire is loupin' hat,
A new heid horseman's kist is set
Richts o' the lum; whaur by the blaze
The auld ane stude that kept yer claes.
I canna thole to see it yet.

But gin the auld fowk's tales are richt
An' ghaists come hame on Hallow Nicht,
O' freend o' freends! What wad I gie
To feel ye rax yer hand to me
Atween the dark an' caun'le licht?

Awa in France, across the wave,
The wee lichts burn on ilka' grave,
An' you an' me their lowe hae seen.
Ye'll maybe hae yer Hallowe'en
Yont, whaur ye're lyin' wi' the lave.

There's drink an' daffin', sang an' dance
And ploys and kisses get their chance,
But Lachlan, man, the place I see
Is whaur the auld kist used to be
And the lichts o' Hallowe'en in France.

The Wise Like Chap

words Violet Jacob

Aye, billies, I'm a wise-like chap,
I dinna smoke nor drink.
And gin I gie my poke a slap
Ye'll hear the siller chink,
My feyther has an aicht-pair fairm
Weel set wi' byre an' stack.
There's mony will obey me
An' tak their pattern frae me,
But Annie winna hae me
An my he'rt's near brak.

My grannie saved a bit hersel'.
She's three-score year an' ten
Wha'll get the profit nane can tell
(An' yet I think I ken)
It's fules wad cross a rich old wife
Sae a' her fleere I tak',
An' tho' it's like to pay me,
Richt little guid 'twill dae me,
For Annie winna hae me
An' my he'rt's near brak.

Ye'll mebbe mind the miller's loon
That was a fair disgrace,
His auld dune was clour'd abune
An' mill-dust on his face.
The gowk! He gaed awa to fecht
And syne cam cripp'lt back.
Yestre'en he passed my grannie
Wi' his left airm bandig't cannie,
But gis richt ane happit Annie,
An my he'rt's near brak.

The Greylag Geese

The summertime is bonnie, an' maist fowk say they like it best o' a'.
But o' there's ae thing missin', the greylag geese have a' flown far awa'.

When autumn comes aince mair, the wind blaws cauld an' nichts are growin' black
There's ae thing sent tae cheer me, the soond that says again the greylag's back.

When winter clouds blaw ower an fowk wi' heids doon collars turned up high
My een they aye stray upward, lookin' for yon lang skein in the sky.

And then when days grow langer the springtime urge is tae be movin' on
But roots can haud ye stranger an' then ye realise the geese are gone.

I envy a' thae wild geese that can jist fly tae countries ower the sea
Tae Norway, Iceland, Greenland they ken the way o' livin' wild and free.

Violet Jacob's *The Wild Geese* **is undoubtedly my most popular song, and is being sung by many other singers, some of them changing its name to 'The Norlan' Wind'. It has truly become a folk song.**

One of the lads I meet in the village inn, said to me in summertime, "The geese are a' awa, Jim, what dae ye sing aboot noo?" That gave me the idea for this song.

The Tramp to the Tattie-dulie

I didn't put a tune to this Violet Jacob poem, but I did recite it a lot, with a member of my group playing *The Tattie-dulie*, **bogle or scarecrow. We always had a couple of old bonnets to put on as 'props' while we performed it.**

Thrawn-leggit carle wi' airms on hie
And jist a hole for ilka ee,
Ye needna lift yer hand tae me
As though ye'd strike me.
Ye're threits abune an' stae below,
But what-like use is sic a show?
Ye maun respect me bogle, tho'
Ye mauna like me!

To gutsy doo or theivin' craw
Ye mebbe represent the law
When they come fleein' owre the wa'
To tak an airin'.
Dod, I'll no say they arena richt
When sic a fell unchancy sicht
Gars them think twice afore they licht –
But I'm no carin'.

Yer heid's a neep, yer wame's a sack
Yer ill-favred face gars bairnies shak',
But yer the likes o' you can mak'
A livin' frae it.
Sma' use to me, it isna fair
For tho' there's mony wid declare
That I'm no' far ahint ye there.
I canna dae it.

Life's a disgust wi' a' its ways,
For free o' chairge ye get yer claes,
Nae luck hae I on washin-days
There's plenty dryin',
But gin I see a usefu' sark
An' bide or gloamin' help my wark
The guid wife's oot afore it's dark!
And leaves nane lyin'.

Weel, weel, I'm aff, it's little pleasure
To see ye standin' at yer leisure
When I've sae mony miles tae measure
To get a meal.
Ye idle dog! Ma bonnet's through
An' yours is no exactly new
But a' the same I'll hae't frae you
And faur-ye-weel.

Back in Time

O take me back in time
To those boyhood days of mine
When Bobby an' masel' roamed on the braes
An' we followed every trail
In Athole's bonnie vale
In the lang gone carefree sunny summer days.
O tae be oot on the hill
When the morning hours stood still
And listening tae the laverock as it flies.
Then over to Loch Bhac,
Will I ever make it back
To hear yon lonely curlew's 'quirren' cries.

At the river Garry's bend
Where we swam for hours on end
And whiles forgot to go home for oor tea
And when the sun gaed doon
At the fire we'd gather roon'
An' the stories that the auld fowk tell't tae me.
Noo the wee hoose near auld Struan
Was for many years a ruin
'Til yon new road it has left nae trace at a'
Traffic flees baith here an' there
On that through goin' thoroughfare
And the auld fowk thay are nearly a' awa'.

Take me back in time. How nostalgic can you get? It gets worse as you grow older. However, I'm not going to apologise, it's just the way I am. This song reminisces on teenage holidays at my cousin Bobby's, just two or three miles north of Blair Athol.

Marag Cnocach

Bob Reid

The wee hoose was near to Inverbhac farm and was called 'Marag Cnocach' (pronounced Crocach), probably meaning 'Hilly Muir'. Bob wrote a pipe march to commemorate it and bring back the happy memories.

Archie's Caravan

While we are still in the bonny glen of the river Garry, here is a pipe tune I wrote about Struan.

Expert Angler

This song was not strictly true of course. I did catch a fish or two, but at the time I wrote it, I began to feel less inclined to kill them just for my own pleasure. So I gave up the 'sport' altogether.

I've come hame clean frae Isla's stream
On mony's the perfect day,
And on evenings when the water biled,
Luck never went ma way.

Chorus
Yet I'm an expert angler
For advice they seek me oot
It's a freak o' nature that ma bag
Has never held a troot.

They've marvelled at my castin',
Or the wie I tie a flee,
When we crack aboot the fish we catched,
I'm afraid I have tae lee.

Chorus

On Rescobie and Lintrathen Lochs
I've never made a kill,
Yet thae braw lochs an mony mair
Hae experienced ma skill.

Chorus

Ae evening on the banks o' Tay
A salmon took ma lure,
The beast wis thirty pund or mair
I played it for an hoor.
An' when I brocht it tae the bank
I thocht it breathed its last,
I stepped intae a big deep hole,
An' broke ma bluidy cast.

Chorus

I'll keep castin' flees in Deveron
Dee, Ythan, Don and Spey,
An' aye think up a story
For the one that got away.

Chorus

The Deein' Stag

It wisna me ma bonny beast, wha's made yer bluid tae run;
O dinna look at me like that, I dinna hae a gun;
An' yer I canna blame ye wi' yer pained untrustin' stare;
A' man's a man for a' that some guilt I'll hae tae share.

A simple climber's a' I am, like you these hills I roam;
But wi' you I never will compare, this is your native home;
I wis hidin' here ahent this rock I shouldna hae been here,
For this is now the season tigh earna beag kill deer.

Ye were standin' proud as I looked doon, and then I saw the man;
A shot rang out you staggered then up the hill you ran;
You neared me on the tapmost ridge an' fell wi' gaspin' breath,
The hunter wha had thocht he'd missed has left you tae yer death.

I canna bring masel' tae dae the thing that's ca'd humane,
But I'll sit beside ye an' I'll try tae help ye wi' yer pain,
An' when yer killer reaches hame an' pits awa his gun,
He'll till his friends the stories aboot a day o' fun.

The next song is less humorous, but
more true than the previous one.
Tigh earna beag is Gaelic for lesser
lairds or 'lordlings'.

I Canna Find the Thyme

I did have a tune to 'I Canna Find the Thyme', but in trying to sing it, it was impossible for anyone to understand my meaning.

It's a poem that has to be read.

I've been hungry in the Beeftub
An' stervin' on the Minch.
I've been in Perth in sic a fog
That ye couldna see an Inch.

I've used a brush tae sweep a lake
Tho' twisna for the dirt
An' I've been tae Coul in sic a heat
That ye could wring ma shirt.

I've rowed a boat on Nevis
An' swam in Lochnagar
An' my erse wis on the Elbow
Aince goin' tae Braemar.

There wis naebody tae pass the saut
On the Table of McLeod
An I couldna sit on Arthur's Seat
For there wis sic a crowd.

In Auld Dundee I've often been
On baith sides of the Law
An' near Arbroath I've seen the
Weetest Flairs ye ever saw.

I've never had a Solway Sark
I think it widnae suit
But I've tried tae wear the border Tweed
Spent a' nicht dryin' oot.

I aince set aff tae try an' find
The Sisters of Kintail
But I found myself in Bettyhill
And landed in the jail.

But I think I'll tak' a Tummel
While finishing this rhyme
Tae climb nae mair high mountains
I canna find the thyme.

Freewheelin' Now

I'm getting ower the hill it seems,
Tho ma hert it still feels young,
But they say when half a hunders here,
Your flings should a' be flung.

But I've some flungs I've yet tae fling,
Before I end ma days,
So I don't want tae hear ye say,
That old 'ye're past it' phrase.

Freewheelin' now, freewheelin' now,
It's easier every day,
Just tak' it slow whene'er ye go,
Freewheelin' down the brae.

I canna climb the highest hills,
I used tae dae sae weel,
But the view is bonnie even frae here,
And ye're just as high as ye feel.

Chorus

Ma eyesight's growin dimmer noo,
And specs I ought tae wear,
But there's some things I see clearer still,
And I canna ask for mair.

Chorus

I ken a man that's fu' o' fun,
He fairly maks ye laugh,
Wi' jokes aboot his new wheelchair,
He's baith his legs ta'en aff.

Chorus

We've aa tae go a different road,
It would get hard sometimes,
So let's try tae help oor neighbours
Tae get ower the stiffest climbs.

Chorus

I was ready to throw *Freewheelin' Now* out, although it had a good chorus. I thought that the three verses didn't have much to say. Then I met this young chap, George, who had had an accident on a motor bike and lost both legs. He was in good form with the jokes, mostly against himself.

Here's one of them: 'I went to the doctor's last week and he said, "The good news is, your high-powered, turbo-charged wheelchair has arrived, the bad news is, it's got a kick-start".

I wrote two more verses which made the song for me.

The Foundry Band

Bert Murray

Speaking about freewheeling, brings my mind to Bert Murray, who I think had a secret contract with the Duracell Battery Co. In his 80s he still was fiddling away like a young 'un. He was a great friend of mine and of the Foundry Band, becoming our only Honorary Member. We had marvellous times together. On one tour of Orkney, which lasted about ten days, we hardly slept at all. He wrote this tune for us about that time.

James and Dinah's Diamond Waltz

While on Orkney we stayed with the Wylie family of Harray, who arranged the tour for us. Bill's father and mother had just had their diamond wedding anniversary, and to commemorate this, a granddaughter had written a tune and presented it to them framed. We copied it and then played it the rest of the tour, much to the pleasure of everyone.

I shall always remember the welcome we received in Orkney and the dozens of brilliant musicians and singers who came along to help us out on our concerts. Good on ye.

Welcome to the Glen

I can't remember much about *Welcome to the Glen.* I think that the second verse is not mine, but that I read it somewhere, then put the other verses to it. Somebody told me the the term for this is senility. I can't remember who.

In spring when snaw begins tae melt
Upon the mountain tap
The burns roar doon wi' sic a speed
And teuchats start tae flap
The sun will rise a wee bit mair
An' keek oot ower the ben
The leaves appear on ilka tree
Sayin' welcome tae the glen.

The Heiland hills are bonnie noo
Alow the summer sun
The birdies sing a blyther sang
The burnies safter run
The summer breeze that blaws around
The shepherd's but and ben
Comes whispering in the stranger's ear
Ye're welcome tae the glen.

The nichts are drawin' in again
The leaves have turned tae broon
An' snaw lies on the taps aince mair
The deer start comin' doon
They'll shelter in the forest
Till spring comes roond again
An' naebody there will bather them
They're welcome to the glen.

The winter wind is howlin' noo
The snaw sae very deep
Maist birds have flown tae warmer lands
An' beasts their winter's sleep
But in each Heiland cottage
The traveller will ken
A freendliness that always says
Ye're welcome tae the glen.

Back in Scotland

When I was young my granddad used to take me on his knee
And tell me of his homeland so far across the sea.
He made me promise to return to his wee croft some day,
"You'll never have true peace of mind until you do." He'd say.

He told me of his father who was killed in a foreign war,
He fell advancing with the men still playing his old *piob mhor*
And his mother who died while trying her best to fight the raging flames
When the landlord and his murdering gang set fire to their hames.

He was just sixteen when he came over here and cleared the virgin soil
And set aside his grief and settled down to years of toil
But he ne'er forgot old Scotland tho' three score years and ten
And the only sadness that he had he never got home again.

So now I'm back in Scotland just as my granddad wished,
I'm looking down into the pool where as a boy he fished
And up the hill the rowan tree still guards the pile of stones
And that is all there is to see of what had been his home.

I'm looking to the point of land from where he sailed away
To leave the country that he loved until his dying day.
Now a big stone from that hillside pile is sailing ower the wave
And when I return to Canada, I'll place it on his grave.

When I was over in America, I met so many exiles or descendents of exiles. Coming home on the plane, I wrote this song.

Another World

One of the benefits we travellers have now is the return ticket. The singer in the previous song had one, but his grandfather never did.

On a visit to an airport, I had a long wait and amused myself by writing this.

I'm sittin' in the airport, I'm waitin' for a plane.
I'm here tae meet some freens of mine
Wha're comin' hame frae Spain.

I got here at the back o' nine tae gie me plenty time,
A cup o' tea, a piece 'n cheese, wid satisfy ma wyme.

But the sorry situation the plane is five hoors late
And in this strange and alien place I'm forced tae sit an' wait.

Although I'm no' that far frae hame it's a scene I dinna ken,
This place is like a different world tae oor hoose u p the glen.

Loudspeakers shout instructions, tae wha I canna tell,
They a' rush through a big gless door that opens an' shuts itsel'.

They walk alang a corridor, they move sae fast but fegs
I took anither look at them, they dinna move their legs.

There's a hoover that a man sits in and drives jist like a car
They scrub the flair although there's no ' the slightest trace o' gla'r.

A robot took ma money an gied me a cup o' tea
But the workin' fowk I spoke tae were jist teuchters like me.

I wondered whit wid bring them here frae their ane wee Heilant hame,
They said "You bide here lang enough ye'll likely end the same".

Good – ma freends' plane's comin' in, loudspeakers start tae roar
I'll be happier when I'm walkin' oot that big self-opening door.

Linda A. Reid

Craig D. Reid

The next two tunes are named after my daughter, Linda, and my son, Craig. They are both married with Linda having a son and Craig two daughters.

You'll guess, of course, that being nostalgic, I tend to reminisce about them when they were bairns themselves.

I thought you would like to see the original handwritten tunes.

For the Love of My Country

Chorus
Tell me what can I do for the love of my country
And what can I say in praise of her name
Just love all the others as if they were brothers
For in spite of our differences we're the same.

I met an old man on the top of a mountain
We were gazing around at the wonderful sights
'Twasn't hard to imagine the whole world was peaceful
We were so far removed from all turmoil and fights.

Chorus

I said is there a land to compare with our own one
And he answered, 'Well each one's unique in it's way
And we all could learn to be more understanding
We could well find the road to real peace one fine day'.

Chorus

When I told him he spoke with great words of wisdom
His smile slowly changed to a hint of a frown
Saying , 'the thoughts that we have when we're high on a mountain
Become muddled up when we're back in the town'.

Chorus

Jamie Reid

I'm Jamie Reid – an Angus man
My home is by the Isla Water
With aching heart I left my little croft
My wife my son and daughter.

The common man has not the power to refuse
When his chief calls out the clan war cry
And my Lord Ogilvie commands a regiment in France
While I await the hour to die.

I made my living working on the land
My pipes I'd play at wake and wedding
And after all my daily work was done
I'd play in the shadow of the steading.

We all assembled on the Castle Green
And the orders were to march away
To win or die for Charlie the Prince
And I at the head, my pipes to play.

The common man has not the power to refuse
When his chief calls out the clan war cry
And my Lord Ogilvie commands a regiment in France
While I await the hour to die.

I never fired a musket nor waved a broad claymore
I only played the men to battle
But the judge, he said that the playing of my pipes
Was fearsome as the cannons' rattle.

The common man has not the power to refuse
When his chief calls out the clan war cry
And my Lord Ogilvie commands a regiment in France
While I await the hour to die.

In November 1746 James Reid was executed, in York, for his part in the '45 Rebellion. At his trial his plea was that he did not bear arms and as a musician injured no one. The jury found him guilty of using an 'instrument of war'.

This story has always intrigued me and made me wonder if I am in any way related to the ill-fated piper who belonged Angus and was in the Ogilvie clan. This song I have written to be sung to the traditional tune of 'The Bonnie Hoose o' Airlie', with slight variations.

The Laird o' Pitmuies

It was at Geordie's Ceilidh in the tattie shed at West Mains of Gardyne. When I first played *The Laird of Pitmuies* to Farquhar Ogilvie, he did a Highland fling on top of a narrow home-made bench seat. Although the Laird had on the kilt, many people didn't even notice that he had an artificial leg. The next time I played it was at his funeral at St Vigeans Kirk. The tune has seen a few happier occasions since then, for instance, Grania's wedding, at Pitmuies, and Ruaridh's, in Galloway.

Pitmuies is a well-known estate, both for its lovely gardens and historical links with the Viking invaders, in the eleventh century. (Prince Muies, of the Danes, is said to be buried there).

The Den o' Aldbar

As I went oot one morning, all in the month of May
The fields they were a bloomi' wi' flowers sae gay.
I wandered thro' the woods, as the sun did sweetly shine
An' doon the Den o' Aldbar the burnie taks a twine.

And as I wandered slowly down nearby the kirk
The small birds singing in the trees, in the sky I heard a lark.
Their song so sweet and pleasant the chorus did combine
As doon the Den o' Aldbar the burnie taks a twine.

The trees in the forest and the crops in the field,
For shelter and the food we eat they generously yield
So a health tae a' the fermin' fowk, come lift a glass of wine
As doon the Den o' Aldbar the burnie taks a twine.

There's the ripple o' the burnie, the scent o' a ' the flowers',
The bonny blinks of sunshine that touch the leafy bowers;
And though I'm jist a wanderer, yet a' thae things are mine,
As doon the Den o' Aldbar the burnie taks a twine.

Aldbar, near Brechin, was at one time an important estate with links with the early Stewart monarchs. This is a traditional song about its famous den, which I altered slightly.

The Den o' Aldbar

Then I wrote a completely different song – same Den o' Aldbar, same twine, same tune. The story here is an age-old folktale with a different twist at the end, to bring it more into modern times. Have you noticed that in this type of ballad, the boy always goes away for 'seven lang years', never six, or eight.

As I gaed oot one morning, all in the month of May,
I heard a couple talking in a field of new-mown hay;
Said the laddie tae the lassie ma dearie please be mine.
While doon the Den o' Aldbar the burnie taks a twine.

Oh no the bonnie lassie said, that thing can never be,
For I've a laddie o' ma ain a'sailin' on the sea;
It's seven years I've waited here while he's been on the brine;
As doon the Den o' Aldbar the burnie taks a twine.

O never fear dear lassie, can ye no' see I'm your man,
This ring you gave me when I left, I've worn on my right hand;
I' here tae claim ye got ma ain, in wedlock we'll combine;
As doon the Den o' Aldbar the burnie taks a twine.

It's seven years I've waited here and would have waited mair,
But seein' wha I've waited for, I'm no sae very shair;
For seven lang years I'm goin' awa tae have a rare old time'
Now ye can bide in Aldbar an' watch the burnie twine.

Auld Ballumbie

Now Henry Lovell was a man
A tyrant of great fame
Lived in a castle stronghold
Ballumbie was its name,
He had a band of cut-throats
Who rode with him each day
And terrorised the countryside
From Forfar to the Tay.

Auld Ballumbie, Auld Ballumbie
Auld Ballumbie of Dundee. (chorus after every verse)

The auld mill at Pitkerro
Provided Dundee's corn,
James Durham was the owner
Auld Lovell held in scorn.
He rode down through the miller's gates
With bloodthirsty crew
They sacked the mill and stole the gear,
The working men they slew.

Now Durham was a lawful man
And he fled into Dundee
And straight'way told the council
Of Lovell's tyranny.
The council sent a troop of men
To apprehend the lord.
They turned around and scattered
When they felt Ballumbie's sword.

I often wonder where we would have been if 'The Shifters' had kept going. This was the first group I was in when the folk-scene was just beginning. Jim Young, Kenny Gall, Tony Vander-Kuyl, and myself, that was the line-up, and there was not a group going could outsing us. We sang regularly at the Ballumbie Hotel, now burned down.

In a local history book, I read of a laird of Ballumbie who, about five centuries ago, robbed everyone he came into contact with. I wrote this song and sung it one night at the hotel. The other lads were not too sure about it, so I never sang it again. The title of the song is the nickname he got.

Auld Ballumbie (cont.)

He carried on his plundering
And made his neighbours run.
He even burnt the house and corn
Of John his only son.
But John was not afraid of him,
He drew his sword and fought
And gave his bloody father
As much as he had got.

John went to Broughty Castle
To see the laird of Gray.
They marched and met Ballumbie
Down by the banks of Tay.
He was plundering fishers' houses
When they down upon him fell.
They struck Ballumbie sairly
Slew half his men as well.

The tyrant managed to escape
Although he'd many a wound,
He fled into the Highlands
Where he knew he couldn't be found.
When he came back to Ballumbie's gates
He turned around and swore.
He'd finished with his outlaw ways
His plundering days were ower.

Who Said 'The Times Are a' Changin'

Who said the times are a' changin', roll on the day that they do;
We're still fightin' our wars though we say we don't want to,
And the conference table's as empty as ever,
And we're only defending ourselves by attackin'
Who said the times are a' changin'

Who said the times are a' changin', roll on the day that they do;
There's the young set who say they know all the answers,
But the answers grow narrow as the young set get older,
And the new young set's shoutin' the same well-worn answers;
Who said the times are a' changin'

Who said the times are a' changin', roll on the day that they do;
When there's banquets and feasts for the slightest occasion,
And a man needs a pill to help him with his slimmin',
When a crust may have kept his 'brother's' son livin';
Who said the times are a' changin'

Who said the times are a' changin', roll on the day that they do;
Will the day ever come when we'll all be together,
Never carin' what race or religion or colour,
And all of God's sons behavin' like brothers;
Who said the times are a' changin'

During the great old 'Shifter' days, I wrote a song in reply to Bob Dylan's hit The Times are a' Changin', but I didn't seem to have the hard neck to sing it, so it was filed under S.O.D. (some other day).

I sing it occasionally nowadays, because I think it's still relevant.

Stravaigin'

This work of fantasy just goes to show what can run through a simple mind like my own.

As I walked in through Padanaram an' passin mony a wealthy fairm
I thocht it widnae dae nae hairm tae try an' get a feed,
I knocked an' wha cam tae the door, a fermer wi' a big 12 bore
He glowered at me an' then he swore tae blast me bluidy heid.

I fund oot in a Farfar pub, a lad had gone there seekin' grub
An' left the dachter i' the club afore he shot the craw.
I learned a lesson then and there that if I couldna' be ower shair
That he wis oot awa somewhere I widna speir ava'.

A mile or twa frae Lucky Slap I gied a wifie's door a chap
An' speired if I could tak' a nap intae her barn or shed.
She said come in an' sit ye doon I'll mak yer tea tak off yer shune,
The guid man's hone intae the toon an ye can hae his bed.

I ate her food an' drank her wine, I slipped intae her bed sae fine
But when the clock struck half-past nine she cam' in thro' the door,
She leapt on me wi' vigour strang, we heched an peched the hale nicht lang
In the mornin' I set aff tae gang far tireder than afore.

An' when I cam tae Auld Dundee there was sae many sights tae see
I thocht I'd stop my wanderin' free an' try an' settle doon
But when they saw ma auld bow tent the polis became violent
An' to my great astonishment they threw me oot the toon.

I wandered thro' the Gowrie carse wi' twa thick ears an' gey sore arse
An' vowed I'd never hae a farce again in Dundee.
For me stravaigin' is the life, there's never ony sign o' strife,
I'll wander frae Caithness tae Fife until the day I dee.

Isle of Mull

My stravaigin' has often taken me to the Isle of Mull, my favourite of all the Western Islands. On regular visits with my – latterly it was, musical companion, accordion wizard, John Huband, to play at various functions with accordionist Anda Campbell of the Argyle Arms, Bunessan.
You would think that a weekend on Mull would be so relaxing that we'd come back totally refreshed. Well, actually we need about a fortnight to get over it.

On one occasion there was to be a big 'do' on the Sunday night and John was going on Saturday. I had to play in Aberdeen on Saturday so couldn't go with him. But he said there would be one boat on the Sunday. I set off on Sunday morning and got to Lochaline only to find that the one ferry sailing was from Oban! However a fishing boat was getting ready to take some divers out into the Sound of Mull and I cadged a lift. After the divers were safely back on board, the skipper made for the ferry pier but found the swell was too big to get near enough for me to 'dis-embark' (in other words 'jump aff'). I thought I was beaten, but he came up with an idea. He dropped me off on a salmon farm tank further out and said he would contact the fish farm-ers. That seemed OK at the time, but about an hour later I was beginning to get a bit worried.

I must have been a strange sight, standing out in the Sound of Mull clutching my guitar case as if I were waiting for a bus. However, eventually, the aluminium speedboat arrived and I got on board after I'd given them a hand to feed the fish. We landed on a pebbly beach and I set off to hitch-hike to Bunessan, but the Island telegraph had been at work and it wasn't long before John turned up in his car. There was a lot of laughs at my expense that night. I wrote this poem on the ferry coming back.

Isle of Mull
You have given me so much –
Delight in your wild beauty,
Laughter and friendship
with your people.
You have thrilled me
With your music
And you give me a great sadness
Each time I sail away.

The Winds of Tiree

Huband/Reid

My boat's well rigged and ready to sail
And I'll cast her away in the teeth of the gale
I long for the time when again I can feel
The summer winds of Tiree.
When last I left that Western Isle
Where people greet you with a smile
I knew, though I'd travel many a mile,
I'd come back to the winds of Tiree.

And now we're passing lone Skerry Vore
Where, on the wind, the sea birds soar
And ahead I can see the high Carnan Mhor
And the beautiful bay of Traigh Bhi
A happy place in summer's bloom
But it has known its hour of gloom
When fishermen sailed out to their doom
By the roaring wind of Tiree.

And now we're tied up by the pier
There's helping hands and hearts of cheer
The wind is whispering in my ear
Saying stay on the Isle of Tiree
It's here I've left the world behind
It's here I know that I will find
In here a sense of true peace of mind
With the whispering winds of Tiree.

I was playing at the Webster Theatre in Arbroath, one time, with John and his Muirhead accordion band. He said to me, "listen to this next tune, I've just written it and I'd like you to give it words." He called it 'The Winds of Tiree' after a rather stormy crossing to that island with the band. This is the result.

The Moothie Man

words John Huband
tune Traditional

This song is unusual in that John didn't write the tune but he wrote the words. In the song he takes the mickey out of me playing tunes on the mouth organ and guitar. I chose the tune for it, a bothy ballad which goes 'lultae falooral aye doh tooral ooral ae.'

When in my youth tae tell the truth, a music man I'd be
Nae fiddle braw nae heedrum haw, would ever dae fore me
Nae saxophone nae slide trombone, or onything sae couth
The moothie's there for ony air, an a' ye need's yer mooth

Sook sook blaw sook blaw blaw sook blaw
Is a' ye need tae mind
For march and reel strathspey, quadrille
Aye keep that an' ye'll find
That Haydn, Brahms an' hymns an' psalms
Tae them ye'll say amen
Just call encore and shout for more
Tae start me aff again.

I took up lessons, jazz and sessions but that was no' for me
I ha'e the feel that my appeal when I jist hae one key
Has fallen, slightly and quite rightly music days are marred
When tell't if you bring oot that thing ye b----- ye'll be barred.

Chorus

At length offence was taken and I landed wi' a charge
The sheriff said 'A noise like that we canna ha'e at large'
I pled repentance but the sentence, worse than death by far
Sixty days of non-stop playing in the Foondry Bar.

Chorus

Fly Again

Huband/Reid

Fly again sweet, bonnie bird
Though you'll maybe never fly so high – mo leannan
As the time we nearly reached the sky
When we were eaglets soaring free.

Then your wings were young and strong
Your eye was keen your heart was brave – mo leannan
You gave us all the love you have
Now we must help you all we can.

But we are dazed and so confused
And your pain leaves an empty feeling
But spread your wings and try once more
We need you back again, we love you so.

Fly again sweet bonnie bird
Though you'll maybe never fly so high – mo leannan
As the time we nearly reached the sky
When we were eaglets soaring free

Then your wings were young and strong
Your eye was keen, your heart was brave – mo leannan
You gave us all the love you have
Now we must help you all we can

We need you back again to lead us
Steer our course both straight and steady
We know that with our love and help
That you will spread you wings and fly again

Tragedy struck the Huband family when John's wife Pat had a stroke. It was a terrible shock to everyone who knew her. She was such an active person that it was hard to take in, and when I went up to see John he was struggling to come to terms with it.

He was writing a melancholy tune and he asked me to try to write words for it. I said that I didn't think I was capable of it and he didn't answer, but when I was leaving he just said, 'do it Jim'.

An Ordinary Genius

22 February 2000. Phones were ringing – non-stop.
"Have you heard."
"Huband's dead".
"I don't believe it."
"Are you sure."
"Sorry. I'll have to go."
"This is too much."

Well maybe it was too much but it was only too true and we just had to face it, Scotland's greatest ever accordionist had suddenly died. There would be no filling that gap.

This song appeared in my head and I wrote it down and sang it at the funeral.

Chorus
You laughed just like an ordinary man
You talked just like an ordinary man
You drank just like an ordinary man
But your music was pure genius.

The first time that I played along with you
On my guitar I didn't have a clue
It wasn't very long before I knew
I was playing with a genius
You emphasised the few good chords I played
You covered up mistakes I always made
My confidence foundations laid
By an ordinary genius.

Chorus

And now, alas, that you are gone
And musically I'm on my own
I'm thanking you for all that you have done
My one and only genius

Chorus + Inst. + Chorus

It's been fun

No Indispensable Man

John Driscoll, my uncle Jack, had come from the village of Cloyne, near Cork, in the south of Ireland. But he loved his home at Kingoodie on Invergowrie bay. I loved visiting him and my auntie Edith (Edie). I got involved in all his projects, like building a greenhouse and a garage, changing the outside toilet into an inside one and squeezing in a bath. It was great fun and he gave me more responsibility, doing the jobs, than I guess I deserved.

He had a baby Austin two-seater con-vertible, which he called 'The Buggy'. I would be about twelve at the time and when we went out for runs I would sit in the middle on the back of the seat, and he would be singing Irish songs that I had never heard before. He died before I became involved in folk songs, and I eventu-ally heard other Irish singers doing them. He wrote poems occasionally and after he died I had some of them. One poem in the pile I liked and put a tune to it. I found out later, when I saw a picture of this poem, framed and hanging on a wall in Jim Reeves' house, that I had to rearrange my thoughts, either my uncle Jack didn't write it, or he was much more famous than I thought.

Sometime when you're feeling important,
Sometime when your ego's in bloom,
Sometime when you take it for granted
You're the best qualified man in the room,
Sometime when you feel that your going
Would leave an unfillable hole
Just follow these simple instructions
And see how it humbles your soul.

Take a bucket and fill it with water
Put your hands in it up to your wrists,
Pull them out and the hole that remains
Is a measure of how you'll be missed.
You may splash all you like when you enter
You may stir up the water galore
But stop – and you'll find in a minute
That it looks just the same as before.

The moral of this is quite simple
Do just the best that you can
Be proud of yourself – but remember
There is no indispensable man.

The Road to Nowhere

O, my name is Rogue M'Coy
I'm a travelling Irish boy
And the road to nowhere is the one I'm on
And I thought that to be so
'Til I met old Paddy Joe
Now my nowhere days are surely dead and gone.

Now Paddy heard my song
Knew my time would not be long,
So he gave to me my noble tinker's name
And placed me beneath the wing
Of the travelling tinker's king
Now the nowhere road will never be the same.

Jamesie Coffey and his wife
They showed me a way of life
Far different from anything I've known
Julie and her Shamus Og
And young Daheen and his dog
Was the family I could proudly call my own.

But there was one black cloud
Above my nowhere road
It had darkened all the sky my soul to chill
A man came to my view
'Twas the ruthless captain whom
I had cause to hate and I had sworn to kill.

But Ailish O'Conroy
Has saved this Irish boy
When she made me let the black cloud sail away.
Now the nowhere road's no more
For the budget we've jumped o'er
And she'll be with me 'til our dying day.

O my name is Rogue M'Coy
I'm a travelling Irish boy
And the road to nowhere was the road I'm on
And I though that to be so
Till I met old Paddy Joe
Now my nowhere days are surely dead and gone.

Another Irishman whom I greatly admire is the late Maurice Walsh. He was the ultimate storyteller. I first read his work many years ago in a *Courier* serialised version of *The Key Above the Door.* My cousin Bob and myself have been 'fanatics' ever since, with Bob a good length ahead of me. Where I read his books, maybe three or four times, Bob's into double figures. One of his books, *The Road to Nowhere,* inspired me to write this song. I would be happy if this song enticed some folk to read his books. If you can find them, you'll surely enjoy them.

We Span the Sea

I came across an old diary in the attic of a cottage, which I was checking out with a view to renting. It had been an Irishman's, and had notes in it indicating that he'd had a hard and lonely time. There were a few attempts at poetry writing. This one I picked on, altered it somewhat, and put a tune to it.

Each year like geese we span the sea,
We fly from home our loved country
And as we leave we shed a tear
For ones we love the ones so dear – in Ireland.

We come across in boat and plane
A nation on the move again,
We work in factory, road and site
Toil by day and sleep by night – in England.

And in this strange and distant place
We see no old familiar face,
No one will stop and say hello
For Paddies they don't want to know – in England.

The months have passed so long and drear,
My time for leave is drawing near,
I'll pack a case and catch a plane
And soon I'll be back home again – in Ireland.

In Ireland, my home.

The Constant Flow Pump

Is this the heart that beats here within my breast,
The constant flow pump that never stops – well not yet?
Is this part of me that makes decisions
And takes me to places where my head
Surely would not have dared?

What is the use of cultivating a clever brain
When this irresponsible busybody overrules
And never listens to the wise old warnings
But marches on regardless
To its own disasters?

I had thought that when my physical attributes were in decline
This turbo-charged happiness and pain maker
Would have given up those mad takeover bids
And gone back to simply doing the task for which it was designed.

I Talk to the Trees

I talk to the trees
Wis the name o' a sang
An' fowk used tae say
That he must've been wrang
In the heid for tae think
He could get a reply
For they dinna hae mooths
Jist like you or I

But I'm no' sae daft
I'll never be catched
Openin' ma mooth tae a tree
For when I'm in the wids
I canna get in a wird
for the trees are a' speaking tae me

This wee poem came to me while working among the trees at Pitmuies. If you remember the song, then you've earned you senility.

It Took You Long Enough

**This is a song for Julia –
say no more!**

It took you long enough to get to me,
If I had only known you years ago
And tho' it took you years to get to me
You sure could also say that I've been slow.

But now we're here together
We'll never have a care,
We know we live each other
The rest of life we'll share.

Chorus

I've known some girls before you,
You've known some boys as well
But nobody I've known who
Could put me in this spell.

Chorus

But I don't mind the waitin',
It comes good in the end,
For now I'm celebrating
A lover and a friend.

Chorus

Three Words

Three words, that was all
He said, "You sang well";
And yet they said more
Than volumes could tell.

The crowd gathered round,
Although it was late,
Just wanted to say
They thought it was great.

He stood at the back,
His face deep in thought,
And practised the words
In case he forgot.

Down's Syndrome inflicted
That big able man;
I wondered the reasoning
In Nature's great plan.

He said, "You sang well";
His face looked so proud,
Then just turned round
And was lost in the crowd.

I wanted to shake
His hand there and then;
It's likely that I'll
Never see him again.

Three words that was all
He said, "You sang well";
And yet they said more
Than volumes could tell.

I formed this poem in my head on
an overnight drive from playing at a
ceilidh at the Mod in Dingwall.

Music on His Mind

A song for Wull Bruce of Letham, who loved singing. The chorus of the song, of course, could have been written for everyone I've mentioned in this book, and countless more, who have all contributed to the way I feel about music. My thanks go to all of them.

I remember well the time
When Wull was quite a singer.
On Saturday you'd see him doon at the village inn.
He enjoyed a conversation and a whisky wi' the lads
But you would see his face light up
When he was asked to sing.

For there was music on his mind,
Music in his heart and in his soul.

He gave it everything he had
He sang just like a lintie.
You'd guess the crowd all loved him
When they shouted out *encore*
And he would never fail them
With his unassuming smile,
It was never any bother
To gie them a' some more.

Chorus

But cruel time it journeys on.
Auld Wull ha had a stroke
And efter that he couldna mind
The songs he'd known so well
And when he has another try
A tear near blinds ma ee'.
I ken that roond the corner
It could happen tae masel.

Chorus

The Guiding Lights

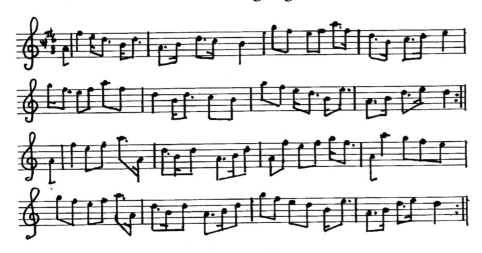

The guiding lights are fading so fast
And now but a memory of the past
Great singers who gave us our culture in song
They are now so few their time won't be long.

We journeyed along like ships in the night
They knew where to go, we needed their light
They gave us the songs and showed us the way
And now they are nearing the end of their day.

And we are prepared to carry it on
To help the newcomers when the old ones are gone
For the guiding lights are fading so fast
And now but a memory of the past.

I wrote this song just after Ewan McColl died and I realised that so many of the folk who had influenced me musically have passed away and it all seems to have happened in such a short space of time. I wrote the tune for playing on the pipes and the song only uses the first part.

Scots Wha Hae

With a few word changes I converted
this song into an anti-war song.
Sorry Rabbie.

Scots wha hae wi' Wallace bled
Scots wham Bruce has aftimes led
We don't need a gory bed
In order to be free
Now's the day and now's the hour
Won at last by people power
The day of Bruce and Edward's o'er
Of that we must agree.

The hand of friendship we will give
And help all others while we live
Never more to lift the nieve
It's been worth waiting for
The flower of Scotland blooms again
But never to lift arms again
In pointless bloody war.

It's Been Fun

It's been fun, I've had a ball, and so nice to meet you all;
And your kindnesses to me have touched my heart.
And as it nears the end, we have gained a few more friends,
And although we all must leave, we are sweir to part.

This beautiful place and its wonderful folk
Will help me to steer through all troubles and strife;
But I'll ne'er be as whole as the day I arrived,
For a little bit will stay here the rest of my life.

I wrote this poem during the best folk singing week of my life. I taught a class in Scottish song each morning, and beginners in piping, in the afternoon at Pinewoods Camp by Plymouth, Massachusetts, USA.

If you don't know the tune to the Margaret Waltz, you'll find it on one of Aly Bain's tapes.

The Better o' a Sang – Jim Reid

Greylag Music, Auldbar Road, Letham, Angus.
GLAG CD01 (Compact Disc)
GLAG CDO2 (Compact Disc)
GLAG MC01 (Cassette)
GLAG MC02 (Cassette)
Recorded at Red Barn Studios, Longforgan, 1996.
Produced by Jim Reid.

LIST OF CD TITLES

I Saw the Wild Geese Flee	CD 1984	Springthyme Records Balmalcolm House by Cupar Fyfe KY7 7TJ
Freewheelin' Now	CD 1990	Springthyme Records Balmalcolm House by Cupar Fyfe KY7 7TJ
The Better o' a Sang	CD 1996	Greylag Music Auldbar Road Letham Angus
Eh'm Fae Dundee	CD 1999	Greylag Music Auldbar Road Letham Angus
Yont the Tay	CD 2004	Greentrax Records Edinburgh